HOW ~~TO READ~~

WORKSHOP DRAWINGS

© Argus Books Ltd 1977

Revised and Reprinted December, 1954
Revised and Reprinted 1960 to conform with B.S. 308A

Reprinted January 1969
Reprinted October 1972
Reprinted   July   1977
Reprinted   May   1981

ISBN 0 85344 057 3

 PRINTED BY   Unwin Brothers Limited
THE GRESHAM PRESS OLD WOKING SURREY ENGLAND
Produced by Offset Lithography
A member of the Staples Printing Group

HOW TO READ
WORKSHOP DRAWINGS

*A practical guide to the
ready understanding of the working drawings
used in the engineering and allied industries*

BY

W. LONGLAND

New Edition revised by
E. W. TWINING

MODEL & ALLIED PUBLICATIONS
Argus Books Ltd.,
14 St. James Road,
Watford, Herts., England

CONTENTS

HOW TO READ
WORKSHOP DRAWINGS

SOONER or later in his workshop career every engineer has to tackle a job " from the drawing." Whether it be a simple straightforward job, or an elaborate one involving the making and machining of an intricate casting or something of that sort, his instructions are invariably in the form of a set of drawings. So, the sooner he gets to understand the mysteries of the products of the drawing office the better, and the more chance he will have of quick advancement.

Every engineering job is first set down on paper, and though the actual manufacture of a machine in the shops may well involve alterations in the original design, the basis is always a set of pencil drawings. These, of course, do not go into the workshop, but are reproduced, as we shall see later, in the form of " blue prints," made from tracings by a chemical process.

At first sight, the man who has no idea of drawing-office work may be bewildered by an engineering drawing ; but let him take courage, there is no great mystery about it. He would not be troubled by a photograph of the article he was called upon to make ; but in reality the photograph tells him very little about the job. The blue print, on the other hand, tells him everything : dimensions, for instance.

The photograph gives him an idea of the general shape, but only from one aspect. It tells him nothing of the internal arrangements, if there are any, or what it may look like from the other side, supposing it to be something unsymmetrical, such as a lathe headstock.

The working drawings are simply outlines of the shape as seen from two or three different aspects. Combined with these will be full details of the internal shape, if it is hollow. Every hole to be drilled is shown, with its diameter and depth, and every screwed portion too, with exact details of the nature of the screw thread. Then the surfaces to be machined, and the degree of finish to be worked, are indicated by easily read signs. The metal of which the parts are to be made can be instantly read also, and if certain of these are to be hardened or otherwise heat-treated, the drawing will show this information as well.

Last, and perhaps most important of all, the sizes to which the job is to be finished are specified ; length, breadth, thickness, diameter, radius of curvature, whatever it may be, all will be found on the blue print. What photograph could show you all this ?

The engineer's working drawing is like the surveyor's map ; it tells him all he wants to know about the work in hand, and photographs, though interesting, are really unnecessary. Until the job is done a photograph is obviously impossible.

Though the information conveyed by a drawing is so complete, it does not mean that it is hard to understand. The whole system of drawing has been reduced to a remarkable degree of simplicity. The earnest mechanic, as yet uninformed on the subject, will find that he can soon understand it, and, once having mastered it, will discover that all languages are open to him. The only differences he will find between British, French, German or any other practice are in the units of measurement and screw threads.

PLAN AND ELEVATION VIEWS

First, then, consider a block of iron, to be made in the form of an exact cube, 2-in. side. Now, everything that exists has three dimensions, which we may consider for the moment as Length, Breadth, and Height (or Thickness). No matter how thin a piece of paper, it still has some thickness. The finest hair or thread, if it exists at all, will have these three dimensions. So, to make a complete drawing of it, *from every aspect*, we must view it from at least three points. These three views may be given various names, but generally they will be called Plan, Elevation, and End Elevation.

Plan

This is the view seen squarely from above, without consideration of perspective. Let us say at once that perspective (or naturally rendered) drawings have no place in drawing-

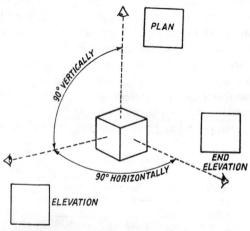

Fig. 1.—Viewing an object in three planes

office work, but we have used them occasionally in these pages for demonstration of various points. The diagram (Fig. 1) shows our two-inch cube in perspective for a start. The eye above is viewing the Plan, and obviously this will be a square, side 2 in. Note that a single drawing can show two dimensions only.

Elevation

Imagine the observing eye to be swung round through a right angle, until it is in the second position. The view is now the one we call the Elevation—a view of the side, in fact. As we are considering a cube, this view will also be a 2-in. square.

End Elevation

Now swing the eye round through another right angle, but in a plane at right angles to the first movement. If this is not quite clear, the diagram should make it easy to follow. The new view is the End Elevation. Again, as we are considering a cube, the view will be once more a 2-in. square.

Of course the drawing-office man would not trouble to make three drawings of such a simple object, but suppose we are to consider a flat bar, 12 in. long and 1 in. square (Fig. 2).

In plan we shall have a rectangle, 12 in. × 1 in., and the same in elevation. It might be thought that these two drawings would be enough to describe the bar, until you remember that a cylindrical bar of 1-in. diameter would also be represented as to plan and elevation by a rectangle 12 in. × 1 in. We *must* have the shape of the cross-section, or end elevation, to fully determine the true character of the bar.

Again, consider a bar 12 in. long, 3 in. in breadth, and 1 in.

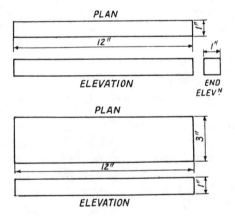

Fig. 2.—The simplest drawings possible

thick. This is a simpler matter, for we can show this clearly in two drawings only. The plan shows the length and breadth, and the elevation shows the length and thickness. No need for an end elevation at all here.

In practice, for such simple matters, as we shall see presently, there would be only one drawing, showing the plan with the end elevation (or cross-section) combined.

We must pass on now to rather more elaborate examples.

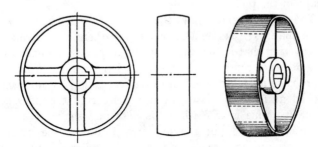

Fig. 3.—Plan, elevation and perspective of pulley

While no one looking at the figure on the right in Fig. 3 has any difficulty in recognising it as the picture of a pulley, not everybody looking at the other two figures would recognise that they represent the same thing. It is a fact, however, and it is how a pulley would appear in a workshop drawing. But why should two figures be drawn when one, apparently, would not only suffice, but besides would be more understandable ?

As a matter of fact it is easier, and therefore takes less time to draw the two figures to the left than the one to the right ; and, what is much more important, it is only by drawing the pulley as shown in the two figures that its true shape and size can be ascertained. Who could tell, by examining the right-hand figure, that the pulley is circular, except he knew it beforehand ?   It might be narrower than it is high. True, circles when viewed sideways appear elliptical, and so it might be guessed that the figure represents something circular ; but it is only a guess when it is thought that a circular body is represented by the right-hand figure. There can be no mistake, however, when the figure on the left is examined. This elevation represents the pulley as seen from the side. Apparently it has no width. The rim, arms, and boss can be distinctly seen, but there is nothing to show that the rim and the boss stand out from the arms. Plainly, then, this figure does not give all the information required to understand the shape of the pulley.

The middle figure shows the pulley as it is when viewed from the front ; its width is given, but there is no means of discovering that it is round. Indeed, it may be thought that this does not represent the pulley as seen from the front, for there is no mistaking the fact that a real pulley is round when looked at from the front, even if neither of the sides can be seen. This is true when the light and shade gives this information, and not the lines which bound the surface. These are arranged as shown in the middle figure, and are all that can be seen from the front. Here again only a small part of the information required about this pulley is given, for only the width is added. But, taken with the figure to the left, much can be learned about the size and shape of this pulley, for the diameters of the rim both inside and outside, of the boss and of the hole in the boss, are there to be measured if required. The widths of the arms and of the rim can be obtained, but not the thickness of the arms nor the length of the boss. The means of obtaining these will be shown later. Drawings made like the two on the left supply more information concerning the true shape and the actual sizes of an object than the single figure on the right. On the other hand, however, that on the right gives a better idea of the general form of the object than the two on the left, even when taken together.

A TAPER KEY DRAWING

The next drawing (Fig. 4) shows an ordinary taper key. The elevation is drawn as seen from *E* in direction of arrow. It shows the length and thickness of the key, but not its breadth. The plan, drawn as from *P*, gives the length with the breadth and not the thickness. The end elevation, drawn as from *S*, gives the breadth and thickness but not the length. Thus each view gives the dimensions in two of the three directions in which every solid body extends. The end elevation requires a little explanation, for it is not apparent at first from whence the four horizontal lines come. The lowest line, of course, represents the bottom of the key. The next, the top of the key, at the end remote from the head. The third from the bottom one is the line where the head commences, so that the distance between the second and third lines is the

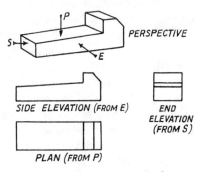

Fig. 4.—Elevations and plan related to perspective

sloping top of the key. And, lastly, the fourth line represents the top of the head. In this view there is no indication that the third and fourth lines from the bottom are some distance behind the other two ; that it is so can only be gathered by looking at the plan or the side elevation.

This is not very easy to understand at first, but when one realises that only two dimensions can be obtained from any view, the practice of mentally combining two views is quickly learnt. Notice also that, taking all three views together, each dimension is repeated twice. Thus, if the plan and side elevation alone are drawn, the length, the thickness, and the breadth can be ascertained and as that is all that is required the end elevation may be conveniently left out.

Or suppose that the plan is not drawn ; then from the side and end elevations the length, breadth, and thickness can all be obtained. Again, the plan and the end elevation taken together will supply these same dimensions, and the side elevation may be dispensed with. So, as a general rule, only two views are required, although under some circumstances it is necessary to have all three.

FRONT AND SIDE ELEVATIONS

It is sometimes asked, when two elevations are given," How does one distinguish which is the front and which the side ?" Generally the draughtsman specifies this on the drawing, but if it has not been done, then think of it in the following way.

The front elevation of a house would be the view showing the front door, and not the back, even though the house measured more from back to front than from side to side. In the case of a ship, a gas engine, or a sewing machine, the same reasoning appl es. But with some objects, such as complicated parts of machinery, it is more difficult to say which can be called a front elevation and which a side elevation, and so in such cases the designer may be allowed to settle this point, and he should accordingly mark on his drawing which is the front elevation. Then, from this starting-point the following general rules hold good. In British drawing offices it is customary to place the plan below the front elevations—that is to say, the view of the top is put underneath the view of the front. Similarly, the view of the right-hand side of the object should be placed on the left of the view of the front, and that of the left-hand side should be on the right of the front view. Although this is where it should be if the plan is below the front elevation, yet sometimes the side elevation is placed on the same side of the front elevation as that from which it is seen. When the front elevation is large and covered with lines, the arrangement of the side view on the side from which it is seen is distinctly useful for rapid and accurate reading of the drawing. When the plan is placed *below* the front elevation, the eye has to cross the elevation from the top to the bottom, and then the space between these views, before points in the elevation can be connected with points in the plan. Thus it would seem an advantage to place the plan *above* the elevation instead of below it, and at the same time place the side elevation on that side from which it is viewed, as in Fig. 4a.

From the foregoing it will be seen that there can be these arrangements of views :—

(1) The plan *below* the front elevation and the side elevation placed on the opposite side to that from which it is seen, as in Fig. 4.

(2) The plan *above* the front elevation and the side elevation placed on the side from which it is seen. See Fig. 4a.

(3) The plan *below* the front elevation and the side elevation on that side from which it is seen.

Carefully note this last method. It combines parts of the first two methods. Thus the plan is placed in the same position as it is in (1) while the side elevation has a corresponding position to that in (2). This arrangement is widely used and care must be taken not to confound it with (1).

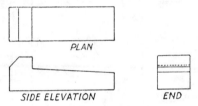

Fig. 4a. Plan and Elevations, American Arrangements of Drawings

THE NEED FOR EXTRA VIEWS

It has been pointed out that two views are required to give all the dimensions of an object, but, as we have shown, very few objects can be completely represented in two drawings.

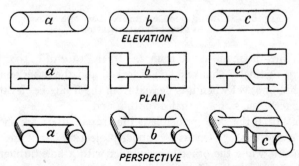

Fig. 5.—One elevation representing different objects

Drawings of locomotive cylinder castings may involve eight separate sectional views. Fig. 5 illustrates how essential it is to keep the views under observation at the same time.

Here three links of totally different forms are seen to have similar elevations. The first (*a*) has a single boss on each end. The elevations of these bosses are seen as circles, while the rest of the link is shown in elevation by lines joining these circles, one on the top, the other on the bottom. In the plan the bosses are seen as rectangles, one at each side, standing out from the rest of the link. The next (*b*), although it has bosses on both sides at each end, yet in the elevation only those bosses which are on the one side can be seen. The plan, however, shows that there are bosses on the other side also,

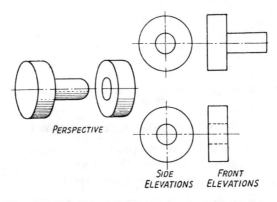

PERSPECTIVE

SIDE
ELEVATIONS

FRONT
ELEVATIONS

Fig. 6.—Showing need for more than one drawing
to give full information

and thus distinguishes it from *a*. In the case of *c*, the plan shows distinctly that one end is forked and the other similar to that of *b*, yet when it is viewed from the front the elevation is exactly the same as that of both *a* and *b*.

In Fig. 6 the same principle is illustrated. Here are shown a pin and washer. One is a cylinder projecting out of another cylinder, while the other is a cylinder with a hole through it, and although their front elevations are entirely dissimilar, their side elevations have nothing to show that the inner circle represents a hole in one case and a cylinder in the other. It may be mentioned that the plans of both are exactly the same shape as their respective elevations. Enough has been said to show that one view must be used to interpret another.

CONVENTIONAL SIGNS

In working drawings there are certain kinds of line and certain combinations of letters of the alphabet about which it has been agreed that they signify certain things, and those only. These are called " conventions," and some common ones will be found below.

∠s	=Angle irons.	G.I.	=Galvanised iron.
Bbt.	=Babbitt metal.	G.F.	=Grinding finish.
Br.	=Brass.	F.	=Machined or turned.
(B).	=Bright (nuts, etc.)	M.S.	=Mild steel.
Bronze	=Bronze.	F.B.	=Polished.
Cpr.	=Copper.	T.	=Tapping hole.
C.I.	=Cast iron.	Ts.	=Tee irons.
C.S.	=Cast steel.	W.M.	=White metal.
G. 2.75″	=Size of gauge.	W.I.	=Wrought iron.

f is sometimes used for " machined." It is put on the line which has to be thus dealt with.

Dia. or ⌀ =Diameter.
L.O.A. =Length over all.
O.D. =Outside diameter.
Rad. =Radius (of curvature).
T.P.I. =Threads per inch.

Then for nuts and the heads of bolts : Hex. means hexagonal ; sq. means square ; ro. means round.

Sometimes the depth of the metal to be removed is indicated by some such means as the following :—

$F = \frac{1}{16}$inch of metal to be removed.
$f = \frac{1}{8}$,, ,, ,, ,,
$F = \frac{3}{16}$,, ,, ,, ,,
$ff = \frac{1}{4}$,, ,, ,, ,,

FINISHING

Some drawing offices indicate the degree to which the surfaces of the job are to be finished by means of signs, which are quite simple to remember. As a rule four such degrees are sufficient : first, a cleaned-up surface, chipped, filed, or rough ground, for which no allowance is required. Next we get what is called a Rough Finish, and this is indicated by one little triangle with its apex on the surface concerned. Finish shown by two triangles, is for bearings, or for appearance.

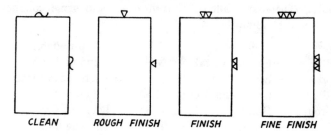

CLEAN   ROUGH FINISH   FINISH   FINE FINISH

Fig. 7.—Indications of finish

Fine Finish, three triangles, is the best finish that can be applied by any means available, and is done to fine limits.

Working instructions will certainly be given on the drawing —such as " Rough Turned," " Hardened and Ground," and so on. Fig. 32 is a good example of this sort of thing.

CONVENTIONAL LINES

We next deal with the conventional lines shown in Fig. 8.

(a) The full line is used for outlines such as can be seen while for those parts that are hidden a dotted line as (b) is used. Frequently hidden portions are omitted because dotted lines do not always add to the clearness of the drawing.

(c) A chain line, consisting of a long and then a short dash or dot, is used for centre lines. Sometimes, however, these are in brown, and then they are full lines. As we are considering the workshop print chiefly, the coloured line will not occur, of course.

(*d*) Sectioning planes, fully explained on p. 37, are indicated by a thick dash and dot line.

(*e*) is a line frequently used to show the outline of something which has been removed or cut away by the sectioning.

A thin firm line is used for dimension lines. It has arrow-heads at its extremities, as shown at (*f*); also the dimension in inches, feet, or millimetres, as the case may be, is placed either in a gap in the line or just above it. This, then, means that the space between the points of the arrow-heads measures the amount given. A single dash on the right-hand side of a numeral figure and just above it means that feet are indicated. Thus, 2′ means 2 feet. Double dashes in the same position signify inches. Thus, 2″ mean 2 inches, while 2′ 2″ means 2 feet 2 inches. And, lastly, *mm.* beside a numeral figure means that the figure represents so many millimetres. Thus, 292 *mm.* means 292 millimetres. This is the metric or French system of measurement, and dimensions are usually given in millimetres only and not centimetres. A little circle, thus, °, signifies degrees of angle, and may frequently be met with. Thus, 90° is a right angle.

The dimension lines are sometimes placed as shown in Fig. 8, left, on the view to be dimensioned ; and sometimes as on right, where the dimension line is taken up clear of the

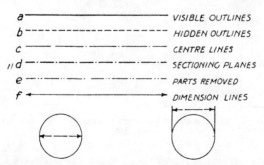

Fig. 8.—Standard lines used in workshop drawings

view, and lines, called witness lines, extend from that part of the view which is to be dimensioned to the dimension line. Both mean the same thing—namely, that the size of the object shown is that given in or above the dimension line.

The dimensions are, perhaps, the most important part of a drawing, and should be so placed that the sizes of all parts can be readily ascertained. But they must not be so crowded together that one may be mistaken for another, so sometimes it happens that dimensions which might reasonably have been placed near together are found some on one view and some on another. If, then, a dimension cannot be found where it is expected, do not conclude that it has been left out, but search for it on the remaining views.

MATERIALS SHOWN BY "HATCHING"

When it is necessary to see the shape of the inside of an object it is usual to draw a view having a part cut away. Another convention is used to show which are solid portions having been cut through. This consists of drawing a series of sloping lines across these portions, and the name given to the lines is "hatching." In some cases advantage is taken

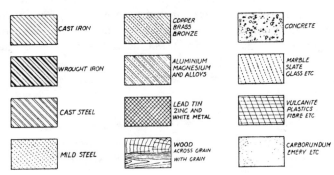

Fig. 9.—Showing methods of indicating nature of materials in section

of this to show the materials of which the parts are made by using a particular hatching for each material in common use.

These are given here and should be committed to memory—not a difficult matter when a comparison is made of the hatchings used for materials which belong to family groups. Thus, cast iron is represented by a series of parallel lines of uniform width, and wrought iron is distinguished by the lines being alternately thick and thin, while cast steel has a series of fine double lines. Next, brass, bronze, and copper are related to one another, and so their hatchings are the same, consisting of alternate full and dotted lines, while that of aluminium and other kindred metals consists of doubled and dotted lines.

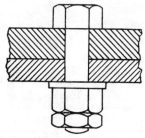

Fig. 10.—Hatching two sections in contact

White metal is full double-crossed lines. These are followed by the hatching for wood, which suggests that material. Concrete also bears some resemblance to the actual thing. Lastly, the hatching for a liquid consists of horizontal lines of unequal lengths drawn across the vessel containing it.

These special hatchings are not universally used, although hatching is always used when a cut portion of an object is to be represented, except when the drawing is coloured.

When only one style of hatching is used for all materials, that shown for cast iron is nearly always adopted. Two separate pieces, shown in contact, are always hatched in with lines running in opposite directions (Fig. 10). Various examples of this are to be found in the illustrations.

MATERIALS SHOWN BY COLOURS

Though the workshop man will not be called upon to work from coloured drawings, he will often meet with them, especially if he attends (as all good men should) the mutual improvement classes. We make no apologies, therefore, for inserting a list of the customary colours so employed. Here they are :

Cast Iron	Payne's Grey (a blue grey).
Wrought Iron	Prussian Blue.
Cast Steel	Purple.
Mild Steel } Special Steel }	Crimson Lake.
Copper	Vermilion.
Bronze, Brass, etc. ...	Yellow.
Aluminium, Magnesium, and Kindred Alloys } ...	Light Bluish Green.
Lead, Tin, Zinc, and White Metals } ...	Dark Bluish Green.
Concrete	Grey.
Masonry	Ochre.
Brickwork...	Venetian Red.
Wood	Brown.
Vulcanite, Mica, Fibre, Bakelite, etc. }	Olive Green.
Grinding Wheels, Emery, Carborundum, etc. }	Olive Green.
Water	Blue.
Marble, Glass, Slate, Porcelain } ...	Grey.

COLOURS USED IN PIPE-WORK

There is also a standard colouring for pipe-work to indicate the fluid the pipes carry. Unless a key on the drawing shows a special colouring system, these should be assumed :

Live Steam	Red.
Exhaust Steam	Black.
Sea Water	Sea Green.
Fresh Water	Blue.
Refrigerating System	Grey.

Air	...	...	...	...	White.
Oil Fuel ...	...	...	...	Brown.
Lubricating Oil ...	...	...	...	Yellow.

" BLOCKING-IN "

If the portion which has been cut is very narrow, it is usually represented as shown at *a* and *b* in Fig. 11.

Shading of this sort is said to be " blocked in " and not hatched. Notice that a white line runs along the tops and left-hand sides of all parts. The advantage of this is seen in *b*, which is a section of a single-riveted lap joint, for if there were no white lines about each of the plates, which are

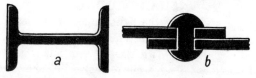

Fig. 11.—Example of blocking-in

riveted together, then the parts of the plates which overlap would show as one block of metal. Now, however, it can be seen distinctly that there are two plates riveted. The reason for putting the white lines just where they are is that the light is supposed to shine on the view at an angle from the left, and those parts on which it shines are distinguished by having the white line on them, while the other parts which are in the shade are without it. Thus the outside of the flange to the left in *a*, Fig. 11, has a white line along it, for it is fully in the light, but the inside of the same flange is without, because no light is upon it here. The top of the web is supposed to be in the full light, for although the flange would in reality screen a part of the web, yet it is assumed that it does not, and so the web has a white line along its whole length. The under side, however, has the thickness of the metal between it and the light, and so is in the shade, and, therefore, without a white line

Then the inside of the flange to the right is in the light, and, therefore, is bounded by a white line, while the outside, being totally in the shade, has no such line about it. Notice that here, again, the other parts of the section are assumed to have no power of putting any part of this flange in the shade, otherwise the lower part of this flange would be screened from the light by the web.   This is also seen in *b*, Fig. 11.   For here one plate covers up a part of the other, and yet there is a white line between them, which line belongs to the lower plate, and has been shown as though the upper plate were not there. The same can be said concerning the white lines between the rivet and the plates.   The line to the left belongs to the rivet but the one to the right is on the plates, for the light is supposed to shine on the right of the hole, while its left is in the shade.

SHADE LINING

The supposition that the light shines on a view from the left-hand upper corner is sometimes used in the case of ordinary plans and elevations.   With these a thin line is used to show where the light is falling, while a thicker line shows the parts in shade.   It has this advantage, that one can tell at a glance if the line in question is on the outside or the inside.

This is called shade lining, and is illustrated in Fig. 12. Notice that here again each part is independent of any other, so far as light and shade are concerned.   Thus the shank of the pin does not thrown any part of its head into the shade.   Consider Figs. 6 and 12 together, and compare the side elevations of the former with the plans of *a* and *b*.   In Fig. 6 they are both the same, but in Fig. 12 the inner circle is thicker on its lower part in *a* and on its upper part in *b*.   The reason is that in *a* there is a cylinder standing on another, and that the light shines on the left-hand upper part of the top cylinder and thus the right-hand lower part is in the shade and is therefore thickened to show it ; while in *b* there is a hole through a cylinder and here the light shines on the right-hand lower part of the hole, leaving the left-hand upper part in the shade, for which reason this is also thickened up.   The outer circles represent the outside of a cylinder in both cases, and are therefore both thickened in the same part.   Thus at a glance the plan in *a*, Fig. 12, can be seen to be that of a cylinder standing on another, because the thickened parts are both on the same side of the circles, while the plan in *b*, Fig. 12, is that of a hollow cylinder, because the thickened part of the inner circle is opposite to that of the outer circle. At *c*, Fig. 12, is shown a view representing *b*, Fig. 12, cut in half, and the front portion removed. It is called a section ; but more about this will come later. Notice, however, that the cut parts are hatched ; which is the conventional method of showing that it is cut, as we have explained.

Observe the disposition of the thick and thin lines. Thus, examining the vertical lines first, that farthest to the left is thin, because the light is shining full upon it ; the next is thick, being in the shade, by reason of the thickness of metal between it and the light ; the third from the left is thin, being in the light, because it is the side of the hole remote from the source of light ; while the fourth from the left is thick, being the outside of the cylinder, and thus having the thickness of metal between it and the light.

It all comes to this, that in the case of the outside of an

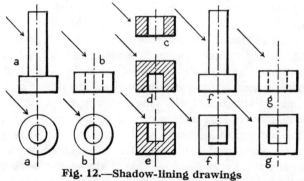

Fig. 12.—Shadow-lining drawings

object the lines nearer the source of light are thin, while those which are farther away are thick, and that in the case of a hole or hollow the opposite holds good. Of the horizontal lines (*c*), the top ones are thin, and all those which have solid metal between them and the light are thick. It may be pointed out here that *c*, Fig. 12, would be the section of a cylinder with a rectangular hole in it, or a rectangular mass with either a rectangular or a round hole in it.   So that *c* being the section of all these different shapes, there must be another view given before the actual shape can be ascertained. And this other view must be the plan, for either or both the elevations would be useless.

Next let us imagine a case in which the hole, instead of going right through as in *c*, goes only a part of the way, as in *d*, Fig. 12.   There the same remarks apply to the vertical lines as were made about the same lines in *c*.   Of the horizontal lines, the one across the top is thin because it is most certainly in the light ; that across the top of the hole is thick because a mass of metal comes between it and the light ; and as the same applies to the line across the bottom of the cylinder it is thick also.   If, however, *d* be turned upside down, then, while the vertical lines remain as they were before, the horizontal ones have changed positions. This is shown at *e*.

Thus lines on any object may be thick or thin according to their position relative to the light.   Going on to *f*, here is an elevation similar to that in *a*, but the plan shows that its shape is totally different. It can be seen that there are two rectangular prisms, one standing on the other (a prism is a solid, having as its ends equal, similar, and parallel plane figures and the sides of which are parallelograms).   It is said to be rectangular when the angles of the plane figures at its ends are all right angles. This is sometimes spoken of as a square, but this expression is correct only when all the sides of the end figures are equal. Returning to *f*, it will be seen that the right-hand and lower sides are thickened, while the left-hand and upper sides are thin ; the reason being that the rays of light are supposed to come from a source in the direction of the upper left-hand corner as before.

In *g* the elevation is similar to that of *b*, but there again the plan shows that the actual shape is very different. In this plan, because there is a hole through the mass of metal, top and left-hand sides of the inner rectangle are thick, while the other two are thin. The shade lines on the outer rectangle are in the same positions as those in the outer rectangle (f), and for the same reasons Thus it is seen that shade lines often help considerably in the reading of a drawing. The reason why they are not universally used is that it is tedious work for the draughtsman to put them in all drawings, and takes an appreciably longer time.

INTERNAL DETAILS

From neither the plan nor the elevations can the shape of the inside be discovered, so that if this is required another view must be drawn. This is obtained by supposing the object to be cut in two parts and one of them removed ; then on looking at the other the interior can be seen. This is called a section ; if the cut is taken downwards the view is called a sectional elevation ; if taken across it is called a sectional plan. Not only does the section show the interior of an object, but sometimes it is essential to interpret the other views.

THE USE OF SECTIONAL VIEWS

In Fig. 13 are shown the front and side elevations of a steam-engine piston ; to the right of these are three sectional eleva-

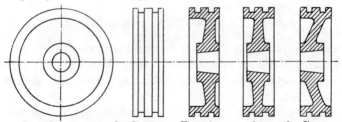

Front Elevation   Side Elevation   Three Alternative Sectional Side Elevations
Fig. 13.—Steam-engine piston

tions, to each of which the front and side elevations might belong, for, tracing out the corresponding parts in each section, it will be found that the front and side elevations of all three are the same. Thus the hole through which the piston rod passes is seen as the innermost circle in the front elevation. Next the outside of the boss is another circle. Following this there is a circle representing the inside of the rim of the piston, while yet another circle represents the outside of the rim.

All of these appear in the front elevation, but there is nothing to show where the web is located. Neither does the side elevation give the required information, for the rim of the piston only is shown. Thus, a sectional elevation is required.

The information might have been given by dotted lines on the side elevation, but it is much more clearly conveyed by the section. At first sight it may not be quite clear why the vertical lines joining the ends of the sections of the rim are shown on the sectional views. Yet when it is remembered that these are views of a piston cut in halves, and that there still remains a part of the piston behind the part which has been cut, it will be seen that these lines represent the back half of the rim—seen on the inside, however, and not on the outside, as shown in the side elevation. If these vertical lines were left out of the views, then they would be sections and not sectional elevations. As a piston is round, these views may equally be called sectional plans, for the latter are exactly the same shape.

A MORE ELABORATE EXAMPLE

In Fig. 14 are shown the front and side elevations and also a sectional elevation of a shaft coupling. From the side and front elevations can be found all that is required concerning the exterior of the coupling. The diameter and width of the flanges, the diameter and length of the bosses, the number and position of the bolts, all are to be found on these, but there are no means of ascertaining how the flanges are fixed to the shafts, nor indeed the length of the shaft in the flanges.

If these things are to be known, then another view must be drawn. A section, either in plan or elevation, fulfils the requirements of this view. The sectional elevation shown (it might be a sectional plan also) has been so chosen that it passes through two bolts, and, besides that, it exposes to view the keys by which the shafts are fixed to the flanges. Although the section passes through the bolts, they are not shown in section, and the same can be said about the shafts. You will remember that we said all solids when cut are, by convention, to be hatched, and none of these are. Besides this, it will be seen on close examination that the bolt-heads and the nuts

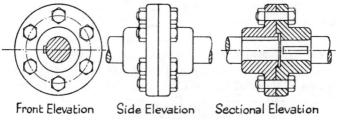

Front Elevation   Side Elevation   Sectional Elevation

Fig. 14.—Shaft coupling

are shown exactly the same in both the section and the front elevation.

Why is this? It is because time and labour are valuable ; consequently there is no need to elaborate a drawing needlessly. We know quite well that only a bolt and nut would be used to fasten the two halves of the coupling, and that each half of the coupling is carried on a shaft. Therefore there is no need to section or hatch a part when its identity is obvious. The draughtsman must always be precise and accurate, but to split hairs is not part of his work. So, then, bolts, nuts, shafts, spindles, rods, and all such things which can be understood even when not cut in halves are left in elevation, while all the rest is in section. In this sectional elevation the keys can be seen, that on the left-hand shaft being on the top of it, and that on the right-hand one being at its middle. Also, one flange is recessed, while the other has a projection fitting in this recess. This is to keep the shafts in line.

SCREWS AND SCREW THREADS

The draughtsman has a standard conventional way of indicating various mechanical details, amongst which must be mentioned screws and screw threads. There is not much difficulty about recognising these, but it is necessary to recognise the difference between right- and left-hand threads at once. Don't get caught by the difference between external and internal threads in this respect ! Here is a selection of the usual representations (Fig. 15).

Where the draughtsman has had to get out his drawing in a hurry, the simple arrangements on the right-hand side are often used, indicating the bottom of the threads in dotted lines.

The only occasion when thread contours are shown is in drawing a section to show a hidden detail such as a drilled hole, and it is not always done then. Special threads, such

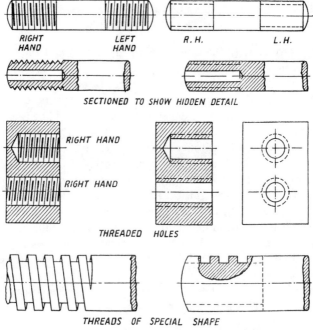

Fig. 15.—Indications of screw threads

as square ones, are drawn in detail, and it may be that they will be fully dimensioned.

The abbreviations most commonly met with on the drawing are easily understood ; thus, T.P.I. means threads per inch.

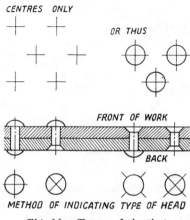

Fig. 16.—Types of riveting

B.A., B.S.F., B.S.W., or Whitworth are well known, of course.

Rivets may be drawn in as circles, or they may be shown as cross-lines to indicate the placing of centre holes.

Common methods of riveting are shown in Fig. 16.

GEAR WHEEL DRAWINGS

An important detail, sure to crop up sooner or later, is the gear wheel. There are so many forms of gear in use to-day that we cannot illustrate them all, but a few standard methods employed in representing them must be included.

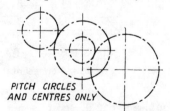

Fig. 17.—Simplest indication of gears

The most important detail about any gear wheel is its pitch circle, for this is the diameter that governs its value, or gearing power. So, if the draughtsman merely shows two circles of lines and dots (as in Fig. 17) that is what they indicate. He may go further, as in Fig. 18, and put in firm lines to show

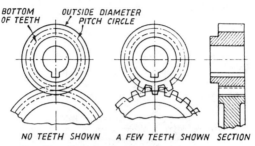

Fig. 18.—Development of gear details

the outer diameters, the outside measurements of the finished wheels, and full lines for the bottoms of the teeth.

Going still further, he may put in some of the teeth—a few to each wheel at the points of contact. Not often will you find all teeth drawn in—time is too short for that ! Note, of course, that centre lines are invariably shown.

Bevel wheels are a little more elaborate and must be drawn a little more fully, but to draw their teeth is to crowd in

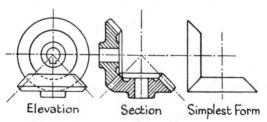

Fig. 19.—Representations of bevel wheels

confusing detail, so it is not often done. Here are bevel wheels in elevation and section (Fig. 19).

Worms and worm wheels also present difficulties, and unless the drawing is specifically one of a worm or wheel for actual manufacture it will be indicated as we have shown it, with its special features mentioned alongside. The dotted

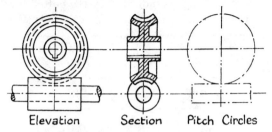

Elevation   Section   Pitch Circles

Fig. 20.—Worm gear conventions

line drawing is the simplest arrangement, and here the pitch circles are intended, as with ordinary gears (Fig. 20).

SOME MISCELLANEOUS DETAILS

There are numerous other details that it is quite unnecessary to draw out fully, as their form is sufficiently well known. Springs, for instance. These may be drawn if they are only short ones, such as motor-engine valve springs, or they may be indicated in section as we have shown here. Tension springs we also add to the examples, and so long as the type or loop or hook end is clearly set down, the rest of the spring

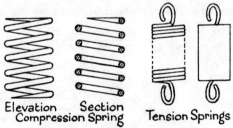

Elevation   Section   Tension Springs
Compression Spring

Fig. 21.—Indication of springs

can be shown just as the draughtsman's fancy dictates (Fig. 21).

When sectioning shafts, tubular or solid, a curved shape is used ; it may be in a figure-of-eight shape, only half of which is cross-hatched. A transverse hole has been drilled through this length of shafting, as indicated by the dotted lines ; the little oval in firm line is the visible end ot the hole (Fig. 22).

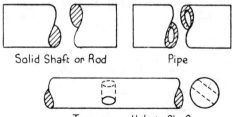

Solid Shaft or Rod   Pipe

Transverse Hole in Shaft

Fig. 22.—Shafts and pipes

The end of the round shaft may also be indicated by an irregular shape, with hatching across it, as shown in Fig. 15, illustrating screw threads. By thus indicating the section it is to be assumed that it is round in shape without troubling to draw an end elevation of it.

A square shaft would be shown by a hatched rectangle.

THE USE OF PART SECTIONS

Occasionally, a part of an object is in section, as shown in the detail showing a square thread in Fig. 15. This part has a wavy line round about it, which is to show that this is the only

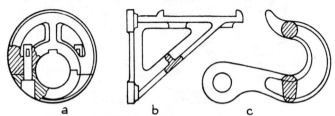

a   b   c

Fig. 23.—Three details to show part-sectioning

part in section. This is usually done when it is only a local detail which it is desired to show. Thus, a shaft might be cut away round about the key to show how much of the key is sunk into the shaft ; and as this is all that is needed, the rest of the shaft is left in elevation. Notice that even here the key would not be shown in section.

This part-sectioning is often used to show some hidden detail, such as a hole drilled into the end of a pin or shaft. An example is shown to illustrate this in Fig. 15.

At (a), Fig. 23, is another illustration of the use of partial sections. This is a front elevation of an eccentric sheave. It is divided right across into two parts, so that it can be put on the crankshaft, and these parts are then held together by means of the two pins and cotters, one pair on each side as shown. And here a partial section is all that is needed to show the shape and size of these pins, and also how they are held in place.

Frequently by drawing a section of a part on its elevation, a *sectional* plan or elevation is rendered needless. This is illustrated in (b), Fig. 23, which shows the elevation of a wall bracket. On it is placed a section of the inclined part to show its shape. Another example of this is seen in (c), Fig. 23, which is the front elevation of a crane hook. The sections show very clearly its varying form. Each is a section on the line dividing the section into halves. It must be clearly understood that these are sections, and not sectional elevations, and that they have no right to be where they are, but are placed on the elevation of the parts, of which they are the sections, for convenience.

On examining Fig. 24, which shows the elevations and sectional elevations of a friction clutch, it will be seen that both the side elevation and the sectional elevation are symmetrical about horizontal centre lines. This means that in each view there are lines above the centre line which have lines below it corresponding to them in length and position, which simply means that twice as much work as need be has been spent upon the drawing. If only half of each elevation were drawn combined as shown at (c), all the information given in the two views would be obtained.

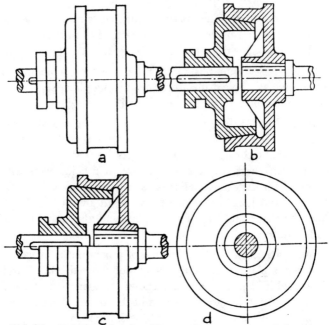

Fig. 24.—Friction clutch : illustrating a compound drawing

This means of economising space and labour is often adopted. A view such as this means that if the section were extended below the centre line the part above it would be repeated, while if the elevation shown below the centre line were extended above it, then it also would be repeated. When this is once grasped, there is not much chance of being led astray by one of these compound views. To the right of this compound view the front elevation of this clutch is shown.

It is noteworthy that the view is the front elevation of the friction clutch as it actually is, and not a front elevation of the other view shown with it, for if it were, then the upper right-hand quadrant (a quarter of a circle is thus named) should not be there. This quarter is shown by the two lines at right angles on the front elevation. This holds good both for plans and elevations given with sections : that the plan or the elevation is the whole plan or elevation of the body to be represented and not the plan or elevation of the section as drawn. This is perhaps at first rather confusing, yet it is quite reasonable, for the real shape of the object is required, irrespective of any sections which have been made of it.

SECTIONS AT SPECIAL PLACES

All sections which have up to now been examined have been on a centre line—that is to say, the object has been assumed to be cut in halves. If it were necessary, however, the section line could be taken anywhere else, in which case it is usual to write beneath it that the view is a section on such and such a line. If attention be paid to the position of the line on which the section is made, then no difficulty will be met with in understanding it, for all the remarks which have been made concerning a section apply to this one also.

Occasionally, however, it happens that the line on which the section is made is not a straight one ; which, of course, means that the sectional view is composed of two or more sections, one being farther forward than the other, or, as it is said, in different planes. This is shown in Fig. 25, but before it is examined for the purpose of explaining the section, a few words may be given concerning what it represents.

A CRANK-SHAFT BEARING EXAMPLE

First, then, it is a bearing for the crank-shaft of a large horizontal steam-engine. It must be understood that the steam acting on the piston forces the crank-shaft, by means of the connecting rod, now to the right and now to the left, while all the time the crank-shaft is rotating in this bearing. This rotation of the crank-shaft causes the bearing to wear away, especially at those parts against which the shaft is forced. So that the crank-shaft may always run true, some means must be adopted to compensate for this wear. This is done by making the step in four parts, instead of two, which is the more usual way with bearings. The parts at the sides where the wear takes place are so arranged that they can be forced inwards, and thus take up the wear on these parts. This is effected by means of wedges, by which they are backed. All this can be seen in the drawing.

It will be noticed that the steps are not divided into four equal parts, but that the side parts are smaller than those at the top and bottom, the dividing being so done that they have flat horizontal surfaces to slide on. Behind these side pieces come the wedges, held in place by long bolts which pass through the cap, and these have nuts on them. By screwing down these nuts, the wedges are drawn upwards, thus closing the side pieces inward as required. Behind the wedges are metal pads for them to slide on, and in the plan it can be seen that both the pads and the wedges extend right across the steps up to their flanges.

As for the rest, it is very similar to an ordinary bearing, only, being a very large one, the cap is held on by four bolts, two on either side.

This is one of the reasons for making the section line in zigzag form. The line, as is seen in the plan, commences on the left-hand side, passing through the centre of one of the bolts holding the cap on, and then when half-way across the wedge it suddenly bends downwards, and then bends again into the horizontal passing through the step up to the vertical centre line. Then it again bends downwards until it reaches the horizontal centre line along which it next passes right across the plan.

Thus there are three distinct sections in the elevation : the one farthest to the left is a section of the part about one of the cap bolts, the next of a part of the wedge and step, and the last of the remainder of the bearing when cut along the horizontal centre line as seen in the plan. Each shows just sufficient for the particular plane in which it is, and that is all. Thus a section through any other of the cap bolts would be exactly the same as the one shown, and this, moreover, if it extended farther to the right than it does, would not serve any useful purpose. The same can be said of the other sections, for

taking the one on the horizontal centre line, then if it be
extended to the left of the vertical centre line, all that is on the
right in the elevation would have to be repeated on the left,
which would certainly be useless labour.

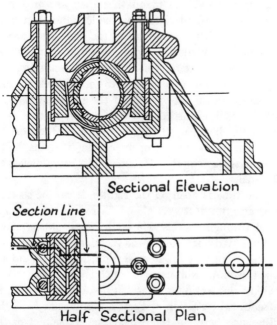

Fig. 25.—Crank-shaft bearing, illustrating sections in
different planes

READING THE SECTIONAL PLAN

As for the half-sectional plan, it is a section on the horizontal
centre line in the elevation, and on that line alone, and so can
be readily understood. Let us return now to the section
through the bolt, using the sectional plan to assist in inter-
preting it.

First, it is seen that the pedestal is hollow. This is shown
in the plan by the two horizontal hatched parts to the extreme
left. Next it is seen that there are two holes for the cap

bolts to pass through, surrounded by solid metal, which the
sectional elevation shows to be of the nature of tubes. These
are joined together by a solid piece of metal, as can be seen
in the plan.   On a close examination of the plan of the holes
in these tubes it will be found that they are of a peculiar
shape, being semicircular towards the left and then bounded
by two horizontal lines right up to the pad. As a matter of
fact it is open towards the right—that is to say, if the pad
and the wedge were removed there would be nothing to keep
the bolts within the tube.   The reason for this is that the
bolt is passed down the hole from the top, and then, when
right through, it is turned half-way round, so that its head
(which is a tee-head, by the way) catches on the sides of the
hole. If the hole were not open on one side, the bolt-head
could not pass through it.   The bolt on its way down is shown
at *a*, Fig. 26.

That the tube is open on the right side can be seen in the
elevation also, for, if it were closed, there would be solid metal
to be cut through on this side, and this would be shown as
hatched. As it is not so shown, therefore the tube must be
open. There can be seen, however, on the right-hand side of
the tube a narrow, white space, which is the back part of the
hole behind the section, and which, because it is seen, shows
that a sectional elevation and not a section has been drawn.
The difference between these has been explained on p. 25.
It will be noticed that this white space becomes wider behind
the pad. This is so because here the part of the pedestal
which surrounds the steps, wedges, and pads is thickened up
so as to form a bearing strip for the latter.

SHOWING A CLEARING HOLE

Notice also that in the bottom of this part of the pedestal
there is a white patch. This is a hole to allow the bolt-head
to pass through. It will be seen also that on the left side of
the bolt there is a white space between the latter and the
hatched part. This shows that the hole is larger than the

bolt, that it is, in fact, a clearing hole. This is confirmed by the sectional plan, for here is a hatched circle showing the section of the bolt, and around this is a white space, showing again that the hole is larger than the bolt.

Still looking at the sectional plan, a vertical line will be seen across the hole between the hatched circle and the pad. This

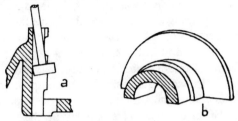

Fig. 26.—Crank-shaft bearing details

is one of the sides of the bolt-head which can be seen at the bottom of the hole. In the sectional elevation, as usual, the bolt is not in section, but in elevation.

As for the section of the pad, there is nothing peculiar about it. It is seen to be a comparatively thin piece of metal, some-what longer than the wedge, while the sectional plan shows it extending right across the inside of the pedestal.

THE WEDGE DETAIL

Consider next the wedge. It must be remembered that the plane of section suddenly alters, and, strictly speaking, there should be in the sectional elevation a vertical line down the wedge, showing where this change of the plane of section takes place. But as this might be misleading it is left out, so the section of the wedge shows simply a piece of metal which extends across the pedestal as the pad does. This, of course, is seen in the sectional plan.

THE FIRST CHANGE OF SECTION

Now, leaving the cap to be dealt with later, the next section is arrived at. Here is shown the remainder of the wedge and the steps up to the vertical centre line. Between the wedge and the side step is a wide space, which, on referring to the sectional plan, is seen to be a recess in the back of the step, for the section line passes through one of these recesses.

Looking next at the parts of the upper and lower steps in this section, three lines are seen to surround them. These show that both the upper and lower steps and the cap and casing containing the bearing are also recessed. Thus the outer arcs (an arc is a part of a circle) are the bottom of the recess in the cap in the one case and in the casing in the other. The next arcs, which are th middle ones of the three sets, are the top of the recesses of the cap, the casing, and the upper and lower steps, and thus show where the cap touches the upper step and the casing the lower one. This is away at the back of the recesses, as can be seen at *b*, Fig. 26. Lastly, the inner arcs are the bottoms of the recesses, in the upper and lower steps respectively. That these recesses exist is confirmed by the fact that the outer arcs end with the cap on the one hand and the casing on the other, while the other two sets of arcs continue right up to the side steps.

Of course, all three are in reality on the right-hand side of the vertical centre line also ; but this section ends at that particular line, and, as will be seen later, the next section does not show the recesses. These recesses are made to minimise the machining required on the steps, for only those parts of the steps which touch the cap on the one hand and the casing on the other require machining. The same can be said for the side steps, which touch the wedges. Thus the cost of a large bearing is materially reduced.

DETAILS OF THE LINER

We come next to the two inner arcs of the steps, which show the section of the white-metal liner with which the cast-iron steps are lined. On closely examining the sectional elevation, it will be seen that the cast-iron steps are recessed there also, but that in this case the white-metal liner fits into the recesses, and is thus prevented from turning round with the shaft, as it is possible it might do if the friction was great enough.

The sectional plan shows that the cast-iron step is recessed crosswise as well, and that, again, the white-metal liner fits into the recesses. In this case the liner is prevented from being forced out sideways. The section has been taken so as to pass through one of the recesses in the cast iron. This can be seen in the plan. Again, it must be remembered that if this section did not end on the vertical centre line, all this should be repeated on the right-hand side of this centre line.

THE SECOND CHANGE OF SECTION

The third section, commencing, as has been said, at the vertical centre line in the plan, cuts the remainder of the bearing into two parts. Starting, then, with the liner, it will be seen that the inner arc is a continuation of that on the left of the centre line, but that the next arc is not so far out as the second one on the left. On looking at the sectional plan the reason for this is seen ; the section being now on the horizontal centre line, and this line passing, as it does, through corresponding points on the right and the left sides of the vertical centre line, shows that where the section of the liner is now made, the latter is recessed, and hence is thinner in this section than in the preceding one. Thus, by following the horizontal centre line in the plan to the left through the sectional plan, all points can be found corresponding to those cut by the section line passing along to the right.

In the sectional elevation it will be noticed that there are no recesses in the liner as there were on the left-hand side ; which shows that they exist only where the liner is thickest. In this section, also, there is no space shown between the side step and the wedge. Looking at the sectional plan and picking out the corresponding point, namely, the point where the horizontal centre line cuts the outside of the step, it will be seen that there the step touches the wedge, and therefore there is no space between them, and so none is seen in the sectional elevation.

Another detail that this elevation shows, also, is that there are no recesses at all, in the cap, casing, or the steps, for there is only one arc instead of three, as on the other side. Also, on careful examination, it will be seen that this single arc on the right-hand side is a continuation of the middle one on the left-hand side of the centre line ; and this shows that in the former section the upper step touches the cap and the lower one the casing, as far as both of these extend.

THE WEDGE AGAIN

Before examining the wedge, it should be noticed that the side steps have the same slope as the wedges, at those parts where they bear on the latter. Comparing the wedge on the right with that on the left, it will be seen that the former is the same shape as the latter, thus showing that it is of the same section right across, but the upper part of this wedge on the right has a bolt fixed to it, which passes through the cap, and is there secured by a nut and lock-nut. Looking at the plan, it is seen that the section line passes through the bolt, and so it must be shown in the elevation ; here again, as usual, the bolt is in outside elevation and not in section, as it should be, strictly speaking. The same can be said of the nuts.

After the wedge comes the pad, which is exactly the same shape as in the left-hand elevation, and so does not call for any further remarks, except to point out that this shows that the pad also is of uniform section.

CASING DETAILS

Next comes the casing, and here the increased thickness behind the pad can more easily be seen. This thickening, as has been explained, is to form a bearing for the pad, which can be machined smooth ; and by this projecting beyond the rest of the casing it alone need be machined, thereby saving some expense.

The same remark applies to the upper part of the casing where the cap fits on. This section of the casing is in that part of the solid metal which joins up the tubes through which the cap bolts pass (this can be clearly seen in the half-sectional plan), and therefore no bolt is here visible. To the right of this hatched section the outside elevation of one of the tubes can be seen, and that this is perfectly correct is shown by the sectional plan ; for here the cap bolts are on either side of the horizontal line and some distance from it. Thus one can be seen in outside elevation when the section is on the centre line.

At the lower end of this tube can be seen the head of the bolt which passes through it ; and as the bolt is a tee-headed one, the head in this view is no wider than the bolt itself.

THE OUTER CASING

After this the outer casing of the bearing is reached, and this as is seen, slopes gradually downwards until, with a sudden sweep round, it becomes horizontal. Notice that nothing of this can be seen in the plan. In this horizontal part one of the holding-down bolts is situated. Around this bolt is a short tube cast in one with the casing. The latter is strengthened considerably around the bolt-hole—a necessary precaution, for often the nuts on these bolts are screwed down very tightly.

On the outside of the casing round the bolt-hole a boss is formed, as can be seen in the sectional elevation. This is done so that a convenient surface to screw the nut down upon can be obtained. After this the casing suddenly becomes vertical and then as suddenly horizontal again, and here broadens out into a flange on the outside of the casing, which, together with another flange on the inside, forms a wide base for the bearing to rest on. This, of course, extends all the way round the casing. Not, however, that the bearing itself requires this, but the foundation on which it stands, being made either of brick or of concrete, would probably not stand the load which such a bearing puts upon it if the bearing surface were not somewhat extensive.

The outer flange can be seen in the plan, being represented by the two outside lines passing round the plan ; while the inside flange is seen in the sectional elevations, being shown by the two parallel and horizontal lines across the bottom of the bearing.

Nothing has yet been said about the hatched part in the middle of the elevation, which extends down from that part of the casing supporting the steps. This is a rib extending across the bearing from the outer casing on the one side to that on the other, and which widens out into a flange as shown. This rib adds greatly to the strength of the inner casing, which supports the steps, thus assisting it in carrying the load without distortion.

DETAILS OF THE CAP

Now there only remains the cap to be examined. The outline of this can be seen in the sectional elevation very readily, while in the plan it is seen to be as wide as the casing.

In the elevations it is seen that the top is curved, and that this curve becomes sharp at the ends, thus rounding it off. Next, starting from the left-hand side, and remembering that the section is here taken on a horizontal line in the plan through the centre of the bolts, first the bolt passing through a clearing hole in the cap is seen ; that the hole is a clearing one is shown by the white spaces on either side of the bolt. Here, also, the cap fits on the inner casing—but more of this when the right-hand section is dealt with, for there it can be seen more plainly.

There is a boss on the top of the cap for the nut to be screwed down on, which gives a flat surface that could not otherwise be obtained, seeing that the cap is curved here. The boss, of course, is shown in section, for the section has been taken through the middle of it.

It must be remembered that soon after this the section plane changes, but that here, as in the other part of the bearing, no line is drawn to show where this change takes place. As has been pointed out it serves no useful purpose, and might even be misleading.

The next section shows the recess in the cap, as has already been explained, and it ends at the vertical line. It should be pointed out that the section of the oil well is not correctly shown. It is drawn as though it were symmetrical with the right-hand section, which it certainly is not, for the plane of section is behind that for the right-hand portion. If, however, it were drawn correctly, it would look so very odd that for preference it is often drawn as shown.

Passing on towards the right—the section now being on the third line in the plan—the hole through which the bolt passes holding the wedge in place is seen. This is again a clearing hole, as can be seen by the white spaces on each side of the bolt. On the top is a boss, as there was on the other bolt-hole, and for exactly the same reason. After this the cap again fits over the enlarged part of the inner casing. It will be noticed here that there is space between the cap and the top of this enlarged portion ; again this is shown by a white space. This space permits the cap to grip the steps, and thus prevent them from moving ; indeed, this is the function of the cap, and, as can be readily understood, it could not press the top step down on the others if the bottom of the groove in the cap rested on the top of the enlarged portion of the inner casing.

Beside the boss and nuts on the wedge-bolt there is seen another boss and nut ; this one, however, is an outside eleva-tion, and thus must be farther back than the boss shown in section ; otherwise it, too, would be in section. A glance at the plan shows that it is certainly farther back than the boss shown in section, for it is the boss for one of the bolts holding the cap in place.

LOCATION OF SECTIONS

Having at last completed the examination of this drawing composed of part sections, it can be seen that, however complicated it may seem at first, yet, when analysed bit by bit, it becomes plain. It is usual to find written beneath such sections such words as these: "Section through AB," or some other line, as the case may be. When this is so a search must be made for this line, so that the section can be understood.

If, however, a section is shown without any such writing beneath, it may be assumed that it is a section through the centre line of the other view. Thus a sectional elevation is a section through the centre line of a plan, and a sectional plan is a section through the centre line of an elevation.

A drawing of this kind saves much valuable time in the drawing office, for two other complete views would be required to convey the information given by these two.

THE USE OF HALF-VIEWS

Another method of saving time is shown in Fig. 27. Here the front and back elevations of a part of a dog clutch are shown, while below there is a composite view, consisting of half the front and half the back elevations. Thus on the left of the vertical centre line are shown lines corresponding with those in the front elevation, while on the right of this centre line can be seen the lines corresponding with those in the back elevation.

It can be quite understood that such views can only be drawn when the object is symmetrical about the centre line— that is to say, that lines appearing on the left of the centre line in either front or back elevation appear also on the right in corresponding positions. Sometimes these half-views are drawn a slight distance apart, instead of making one view of them. In this case, each has a centre line where it would actually be if the view were completed, and not through the middle of the half-view. The side elevation or the plan drawn with these composite elevations is the actual view in each case, and not that of the composite view. Thus the plan in Fig. 27 would be the same as the side elevation, which is shown, and not be half with the front elevation to the bottom and half with it to the top, as it would be if the plan of the composite view were drawn.

From this it will be clear that if a view is seen which is un-

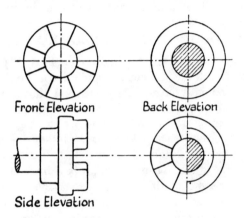

Front Elevation   Back Elevation

Side Elevation

Fig. 27.—Dog clutch : illustrating the composite drawing

symmetrical, and if from the other views it can be ascertained that this unsymmetrical view is really two views, one from either side of the object, then it must be understood that in reality the object is symmetrical about its centre line, and that the view has thus been drawn to save time.

GENERAL ARRANGEMENT DRAWINGS

If an object is complicated and also composed of a number of parts, a view is usually drawn showing the object with the various parts assembled in their proper positions, and then sets of other views showing each part separately. The first view is called the general arrangement, while the others are called details.

The general arrangement is usually an elevation, either front or sectional or both ; sometimes a plan or side elevation is given with it. The details are usually shown in both plan and elevation ; sometimes a side elevation or a section is added if it will help matters. These latter are fully dimensioned, so that all the sizes can be got from them, while the general arrangement has only a few of the leading dimensions on it, and indeed sometimes none at all.

A LOCOMOTIVE CONNECTING ROD

The motion of the connecting rod is complicated, partaking as it does of both the straight line and circular motions. The connecting rod must have a hole at each end, the one fitting on the cross-head pin, often called the little end, and the other on the crank pin, generally referred to as the big end. The situation of one or both of these pins is such that this hole must be made in two pieces of metal, so as to be half in the one piece and half in the other. Then these must be clamped together in place ; at the same time it is necessary to be able to take up the wear—that is to say, as the hole gets bigger by wear, to be able to reduce it to its original size ; being in two parts facilitates this.

A general arrangement of a connecting rod, together with details of all of its parts, is shown in Fig. 28. A connecting rod is the link which joins the cross-head pin to the crankpin which forms a part of the driving axle of a locomotive. The former of these moves in a straight line, backwards and forwards, whilst the latter describes a circle about the centre of the axle.

THE BRASSES

In Fig. 28 the brasses *a a* have been drawn a short distance apart to show that they are separate ; they have also been differently hatched. The hole representing the diameter of the crank pin is of 4 in. radius, the crank pin being 8 in. diameter. They are blocks of metal, usually gunmetal, and each brass is provided with flanges to prevent it from moving

sideways. The shape and proportions of the flanges is shown
at *a* in Fig. 28. Each brass has two broad channels machined
across its inner face and these are filled with a white metal
alloy.

THE STRAP

The strap is a U-shaped piece of steel, *b b*, thickened up at
the ends as shown in the drawing, and of uniform width of
3 in. throughout. Each thickened portion is pierced with a
rectangular slot and two circular bolt holes as shown. It is
because it would otherwise be weakened by these holes and
the slot that the strap is thickened up. The slot is the same
width in both the upper and lower arms of the U but the bolt
holes are not of the same diameter because, to ensure a perfectly tight fit the bolts are slightly tapered to an angle of
about 1 in 96, consequently the holes are approximately $\frac{1}{8}$ in.
larger at the top than at the bottom.

With regard to the other dimensions for the strap it will be
noted that the distance between the arms is the same as the
vertical depth of the brasses, viz. $8\frac{3}{4}$ in. ; also that the curves
at the corners of the U have the same radius as those on one
of the brasses. Obviously the radii of both corners is the same.
The width of the brasses between the flanges will be machined
to fit the strap. Because all these dimensions correspond it
will be inferred that the strap fits over the brasses and that
the brass thrusts against the end of the strap which in fact
it does, as may be seen by the general arrangement at the top
of Fig. 28. From this G.A. it will be seen how the brasses
embrace the strap and how the former are prevented from
moving sideways.

When the brasses are in position in the strap the total depth
they will occupy is only 10 in. and the gap in the strap has a
depth of 1 ft. $10\frac{1}{2}$ in., leaving a space of 1 ft. $0\frac{1}{2}$ in. This is
filled by the enlarged end of the rod itself which is machined
to this length with a depth equal to the gap in the strap and a
width of 3 in., the same as the strap and the width between
the flanges of the brasses.

THE CONNECTING ROD

The enlarged end of the rod has a large aperture cut through measuring 6 in. by 3 in. Since solid metal is not needed for strength this opening is provided to lighten it and so reduce the revolving and reciprocating weight. Beside this it has two holes corresponding with those in the strap. The two holes are reamed out to the same taper as the bolts f. The holes are drilled and reamed at $7\frac{7}{8}$ in. and $2\frac{1}{4}$ in. respectively from the ends of the strap and from the end of the enlargement of the rod.

The main portion of the rod tapers as regards its vertical depth from $4\frac{3}{4}$ in. to $3\frac{1}{4}$ in. and has a uniform thickness of 2 in. At the little end it swells out, again to a thickness of 3 in. horizontally, and forms an eye having a diameter of $6\frac{7}{8}$ in. The eye is bored out to take a $3\frac{7}{8}$ in. diameter gunmetal bush which in turn is bored to 3 in. diameter to take the crosshead gudgeon pin. The rod is lettered c in Fig. 28 and the bush is lettered h.

Returning to the big end of the rod again it will be seen from the plan view of the enlarged end, at the foot of Fig. 28, that there is a forked opening extending down the full depth of the rod end ; and that there are corresponding slots in both the upper and lower arms of the strap. All of these, the fork and the two slots, are to receive the gib, e, and the cotter, d, so that when the rod end is in its place in the strap there will be a clear way through all three.

THE GIB

Examining first the gib e, it will be seen that it consists of a flat piece of steel $\frac{3}{4}$ in. thick having two heads 1 in. high and 1 ft. 1 in. apart, the whole length of the gib being 1 ft. 3 in. The side between the heads is seen to be parallel with the centre line and at right angles to the heads, while the other slopes, so that the gib is narrower at one end than it is at the other. The dimensions show that the width is $1\frac{5}{8}$ in. at the bottom and 1 in. at the top. Thus the taper is $\frac{5}{8}$ in. in 13 inches, or 1 in 21 nearly.

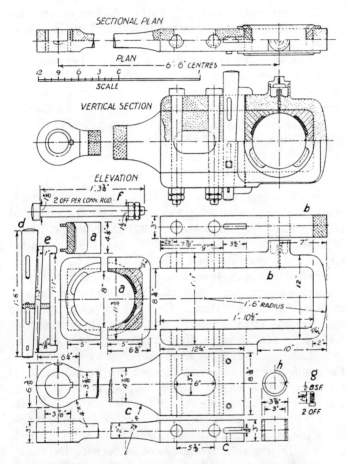

Fig. 28.—Drawing of a Locomotive Connecting-Rod

THE MEANING OF " TAPER "

There is sometimes a difficulty in understanding this latter expression ; it will become clear, however, by examining Fig. 29. Here is shown a taper of 1 in 8, and for convenience we will speak of the units as inches, although all will be equally true for feet, millimetres, or any other units of measurement. It will be seen, then, that the upper figure has two lines starting from the same point—one line is horizontal, the other rises higher and higher at a uniform rate as it recedes from the starting-point. At a distance marked 8 in. on the horizontal line, the sloping line is 1 in. above the former. This, then, is spoken of as a taper of 1 in 8.

MEASURING A TAPER

If the horizontal distance were 16 in., then the sloping line would have reached a point 2 in. above. For $8 \times 2 = 16$ and $1 \times 2 = 2$, and so on ; thus whatever 8 is multiplied by, 1 must be multiplied by the same quantity. Also the taper is the same if the lines do not start from one common point.

This is shown in the lower figure. Here the lines start with a distance of 1 in. between them, and at the end of the 8 in. there are 2 in. between them. Thus 1 in. has been gained, and therefore the taper is 1 in 8 as before. Hence the rule : " Having given the taper, divide the length of the object by the quantity, following the word ' in,' given as the taper, and the quotient is the difference between the dimensions across the ends of this length." Thus, suppose the length to be 1 ft. 1 in. and the taper 1 in 32 ; the quantity following the word " in " is 32 ; therefore, divide 13 in. (which is, of course, the same as 1 ft. 1 in.) by 32. This is 13/32 * in., which, as stated in the rule, is the difference between the dimensions at the ends of this length of 13 in. Thus, if the width at the narrower end is already $\frac{1}{2}$ in., the width at the broader one is $\frac{1}{2} + \frac{13}{32}$ in. $= \frac{29}{32}$ in.

---

* 13/32 means thirteen thirty-seconds, but for convenience is written in figures, with either a horizontal or a sloping dash between.

Sometimes the taper is stated at so much per foot. Take
$\frac{1}{8}$ in. per ft. as an example. This is the same as 1 in 96, for it
is one-eighth ($\frac{1}{8}$) of an inch in 12 in., and multiplying each by
such a quantity as will convert the first into unity—in this
case by 8—then 1 in 96 (12×8) is obtained as stated

THE COTTER

Returning now to the drawing and examining the cotter,
it will be found that it also has one side parallel to the centre

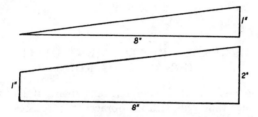

Fig. 29.—Reckoning degrees of taper

line and the other tapering. It is stated that the taper is
1 in 21, which is exactly the same as that on the gib, and from
this, and the dimension of the narrow end, the width across
the broad end can be found. Thus the length is 1 ft. 6 in.,
that is 18 in., and dividing this by 21, $\frac{7}{8}$ in. is obtained, and
as the width of the narrow end is $1\frac{5}{8}$ in., then that of the other
end is $2\frac{1}{2}$ in.

The only other thing to notice about this cotter is that there
are two grooves in it, each 3 in. long, $\frac{1}{2}$ in. wide and $\frac{1}{4}$ in. deep.
That the drawing shows grooves, and not slots or holes right
through the cotter is evident from the section shown through the
cotter d on the left-hand side of the drawing.

THE SET SCREWS

The last detail to be dealt with is the two small bolts shown
on the drawing. They are called set screws, and are used to

hold the cotter in place. To do this they are screwed through tapped holes in the enlarged end, and then, pressing on the cotter, forces them tight against the backs of the holes through which the latter pass. So that the set screws can be withdrawn from the holes after having been screwed down so tightly that the ends may have been flattened out, the threads are turned off at the ends and the diameters reduced below that at the bottom of the threads. Also when they are screwed against the cotter they are apt to burr the latter, and that is the reason for the grooves in the cotter, because then the burr is formed at the bottoms of the grooves and thus do not prevent the cotter from being drawn out of its hole.

GENERAL ARRANGEMENT OF THE CONNECTING ROD

Coming next to the general arrangement, it has already been found that the strap embraces the brasses and the enlarged end, also that the gib and cotter pass through both strap and end. On this view it should be noticed first that the centre lines cross one another at the centre of this hole, and that some of the dimensions are given from these centre lines.

Next it will be seen that much is covered up by the various parts, and that dotted lines are used to show this. Thus the flanges on the brasses entirely hide the inner part of the strap, and also the greater part of both the gib and cotter are hidden by the enlarged end and strap. The gib fits close against the end of the holes in the strap, while the cotter fits close against the gib and against the enlarged end. At the same time, there is a space between the ends of the holes in the strap and the cotter, and also between the gib and the end of the hole in the enlarged end. This is very important, for as the cotter is driven downward it tends to push the gib over toward the end of the hole in the enlarged end. The gib carries with it the strap, for it is tight against the latter, and the strap carries with it the outer brass. This action closes the brasses together, and when this is done it jams the inner brass against the end of the enlarged end, and thereby the hole is made practically solid with the connecting rod.

No dimensions, are given on the general arrangement Fig. 28, with the exception of the length of the connecting rod between centres. All other measurements are shown below on the details of parts.

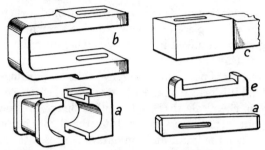

Fig. 30.—Details, in perspective, of a connecting-rod big-end

To enable the brasses, strap and enlarged end with a gib and cotter to be more clearly visualised and their shapes realised, perspective views are given in Fig. 30 of another connecting rod big end more simple in form and construction than the last. It is taken from a horizontal mill engine. There are no bolts through the strap and only one set screw secures the cotter.

SCALE OF DRAWINGS

On the drawing it is seen that the various parts are dimensioned as so many inches, yet it is quite clear that they are not so here. It has been drawn to what is known as another scale than full size. That is to say, a part of an inch has been chosen to represent an inch and the drawing has been made to this new inch. Thus, if it were made to a scale of 3 in. equal to 1 ft., then each inch would be drawn to a length which is actually $\frac{1}{4}$ in. If 6 in. equal 1 ft., then it would be half full size, and $\frac{1}{2}$ in. of a rule would measure 1 in. on the drawing. However, even when the scale is given to which the drawing has been made, it is not safe to use it for taking off measurements on either a blue or a white print. That this is so will be understood after the following brief description of the making of a blue print.

HOW DRAWINGS AND BLUE PRINTS ARE MADE

A drawing is first made with a lead-pencil on drawing-paper Then over this a piece of tracing-paper is stretched, and the drawing carefully inked-in on it by tracing over the drawing beneath. This is called a tracing.

This tracing is next put in a frame, called a printing-frame, and behind it is placed a piece of paper, on the surface of which are certain chemicals that, among other things, are soluble in water, but after being exposed to the light become insoluble. Then the frame and contents are exposed to the light. The tracing-paper being semi-transparent allows the light to pass through it, but where the ink is no light can pass. This light then acting on the chemicals on the surface of the prepared paper changes them and renders them insoluble, while in those parts of the paper which are protected from the light by the ink on the tracing paper the chemicals remain soluble. After this the prepared paper is taken out of the frame and soaked in water.

Then the chemicals are washed out of the paper from those parts where they still remain soluble—that is, where the ink on the tracing kept the light from the paper ; while all the rest, having been rendered insoluble by the light, is untouched by the water but turns an intense blue. Thus white lines on a blue ground are obtained. If a white print is made, a similar but more complicated process has to be gone through.

Lastly, after having been thoroughly washed, the print is dried, which is sometimes done before a fire. The paper, after being soaked through and then dried, is apt to shrink ; and therefore, however, carefully the drawing and tracing may have been drawn to scale, the shrinking of the print spoils all, in so far as obtaining the correct measurements are concerned.

Trust then to the dimensions given in figures, and inquire of someone in authority for those which cannot be found.

The foregoing description refers to a process in which the prints have either blue lines on a white ground or, more commonly, white lines on a blue ground ; both processes have the great disadvantage that in order to " develop " them they have to be washed in water. This wetting and subsequent drying causes the paper to shrink. Although blue-printing is still done it has become almost obsolete and a new process has taken its place. This is known as the dye-line method. The procedure in printing is exactly the same : the tracing is put in the printing frame backed by the sensitised paper, exposed to the light and then developed by being passed through a machine which subjects it to strong ammonia fumes. That is all. The paper is not wetted or even damped ; the lines printed on it are dark grey, almost black, and are permanent. The colour of the ground is dependent upon the density of the tracing paper. If the tracing has been made on yellow or brown, or on thick paper, the print will have a grey background, but if a thin clear blue-white tracing paper, or tracing linen, has been used a white background may be expected in the print.

If there is any discrepancy between the size of the print and that of the tracing the error is the result of printing in a cylindrical printing frame and this, owing to the print having to wrap around a greater circumference than the tracing, causes the print to come out, circumferentially, a minute fraction of an inch larger than the tracing. The error on a print say 40 inches long may be perhaps one-twentieth of an inch, so that to all intents and purposes it is still true to scale.

HOW WORKING LIMITS ARE SHOWN

In most workshops to-day the working limits to which various parts have to be made have been fined down very considerably. The necessity for interchangeability has introduced the jig and the gauge, and we now find that measurements call for exactness within thousandths of an inch. As a rule the designer does not insist upon the finished article being precisely to gauge ; he usually gives limits between which the measurements must lie. For such parts there is a special method of indicating these limits on the drawing, and, to understand them, a knowledge of decimals is necessary. The old system of subdivision of the inch has had to go by the board to accommodate the thousandths of an inch which are so much more convenient for precise work. We shall assume that the reader has this necessary knowledge.

True, many drawings to-day show dimensions thus : say, $8\frac{1}{4}'' + \frac{2}{1000} = 8.252$—a concession to both fractions and decimals.

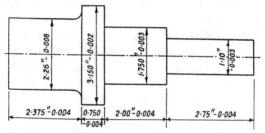

Fig. 31.—Detail of spindle, showing tolerances

Let us suppose that we have a shaft the maximum diameter of which is to be 2 in. The hole in the hub of the pulley to fit on it is to be 2.002 in. diameter ; thus we have an interval clearance of 0.002 in., two one-thousandths. A tolerance of −0.004 in. is allowed for the shaft and +0.003 in. for the hole.

If the shaft is made the smallest possible size, then it will be $2 - 0.004 = 1.996$ in. in diameter. In the same way, if the hole in the hub is made the largest possible, then its diameter would be $2.002 + 0.003 = 2.005$ in. The clearance between the two would thus be $2.005 1.996 = 0.009$ in.

These tolerances may be shown on the drawing in various ways, and so that the subject may be grasped, Fig. 31 is a detail of a spindle to be finished to fine limits. Here the main measurements are given, and they are all maximum sizes, which can be seen from the fact that the tolerances are all on the minus side. Thus the diameter of the flange is to be 3.150 in., but it may be 0.002 in. less and still pass the gauge.

DEGREES OF TOLERANCE

There is another point about the indication of the *degree* of tolerance that it is necessary to grasp. Here is a selection of figures, dimensions expressed in decimals with the allowable tolerances.

12.2 $\pm$ 1. This means that the finished article is to be 12.2 in. long, but it may be 0.1 longer or shorter than the standard. Note that there is no decimal in front of the figure 1 representing the degree of tolerance ; when this is the case it is assumed that it is of the same value as the last decimal place in the standard strength. This is made plainer in the examples following.

1.82 $\pm$ 2. Here the tolerance of 2 represents $\frac{2}{100}$, so that we have a total limit of 1.84 − 1.80 = 0.04.

1.258 $\pm$ 5. Limit is 1.263 − 1.253 = 0.010.

1.3937 $\pm$ 2. Limit is 1.3939 − 1.3935 = 0.0004.

1.3756 + 30. This means that the finished article may be $\frac{30}{10.000}$ (0.003) over size, but not under.

1.3565 − 20. In the same way the article may be $\frac{20}{10.000}$ (0.002) under size, but not longer than the standard.

10.273 $^{+2.}_{-1}$ This means that the finished job can be 0.002 longer or 0.001 under size, a total limit of 0.003.

Another way in which the limits might be marked on the drawing is thus : $\left\{ \begin{array}{c} 1.997 \\ 2.003 \end{array} \right\}$, which is the same as 2 $\pm$ 0.003, only the draughtsman has done the arithmetic to save mistakes in the shop.

It cannot possibly be impressed too strongly on the workshop man that he should master the convenient decimal system, for its use is growing.

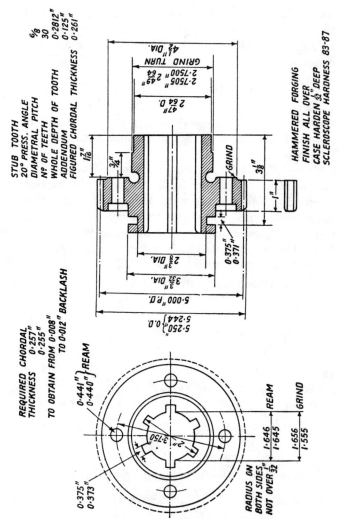

Fig. 32.—Drawing of gear wheel, with tolerances

TOLERANCES IN DRAWING OFFICE

As a final example, Fig. 32 is a detail drawing for the making of a motor-car gear wheel. This is typical of the sort of thing to be expected, for it includes all instructions for the various processes through which the raw forged blank must go, and the degree of hardness that must be attained in the finished job. A number of abbreviations are introduced, though the man who has to work from such a drawing as this will fully understand that O.D. means outside diameter and P.D. pitch diameter. This latter refers to the true gearing-diameter of the wheel, as we saw in an earlier part of this book.

It is also a good example of the workshop drawing of a gear wheel of the sort where no teeth are shown, but only the circles indicating tops and bottoms of teeth and the pitch circle as well.

Reference to this was made earlier in this book whilst detailing the conventional treatments of various objects.

A further point of interest about this drawing is in the machining of the body. Here we observe that the turner is given his dimension in 64ths of an inch, but the finish grinding is to be done to ten-thousandths.

It would hardly be possible in any book to set down all the variations in drawing office practice, but within the limits of these pages we have given the mechanic a good start at a very necessary side of his business. All elaborate things are made up of simple details, and all that is required to understand the big things is a knowledge of principles combined with a certain amount of patience.

ELECTRICAL DRAWINGS AND DIAGRAMS

There is another type of drawing, however, also a plan or layout of items making up one whole working assembly—the electrical circuit. Diagrams of this sort are very commonly met with, and with a little practice are easily read.

ELECTRICAL SYMBOLS

It is necessary to understand certain conventional symbols that are used to represent standard pieces of apparatus, which would be rather tiresome to draw in fully, more especially when their internal construction is elaborate. It is quite unnecessary to draw all the internal details of a motor, for instance, or a voltmeter. To set down in detail the working arrangements of a relay would occupy hours of work, and the same may be said of almost every other item.

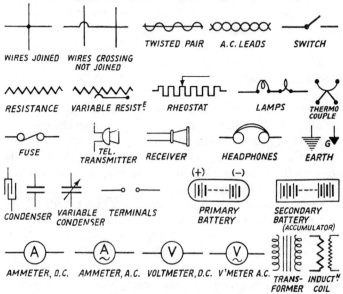

WIRES JOINED   WIRES CROSSING   TWISTED PAIR   A.C. LEADS   SWITCH
NOT JOINED

RESISTANCE   VARIABLE RESIST^E RHEOSTAT   LAMPS   THERMO COUPLE

FUSE   TEL. TRANSMITTER   RECEIVER   HEADPHONES   EARTH

CONDENSER   VARIABLE CONDENSER   TERMINALS   PRIMARY BATTERY   SECONDARY BATTERY (ACCUMULATOR)

AMMETER, D.C.   AMMETER, A.C.   VOLTMETER, D.C.   V'METER A.C.   TRANS-FORMER   INDUCT^N COIL

Fig. 33.—Electrical symbols

So these graphic symbols have been standardised and a formal style of drawing the diagrams adopted, in which all wiring is shown as laid squarely, every line being kept clear of its neighbour, even though they may be enclosed in the same insulation. Several hundreds of the symbols have been devised, but it is not necessary to know them all.

Figs. 33 and 34 show some of them, from which it will be seen that many are boldly drawn pictures illustrating some essential part or principle of the apparatus. Thus, dynamos, motors, and other rotary machines are shown as end views of their commutators with the brushes bearing on them. If it is necessary to be more exact about the nature of a motor, a zigzag line to represent the winding of its field can be added.

All apparatus designed to handle alternating currents is marked with the wave sign ; if this is absent, then it is suitable for use with direct current only. Different classes of electrical work employ different types of apparatus, though these different types really do the same sort of work. Relays are used everywhere, from telephone exchanges to railway

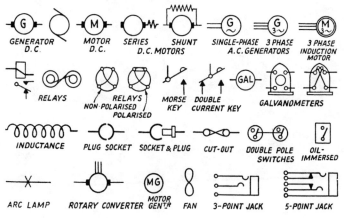

Fig. 34.—Electical symbols

locomotives, and just as their outward form is different, so the symbol will be. Polarised and non-polarised relays are used in telegraphic work.

In conclusion, it should be mentioned that a large number of electrical items are symbolically represented by a circle or a square with letters inside, the initials of the item. Thus we have in our list GAL for a galvanometer, MG for a motor generator. When making up a diagram of the sort where a considerable number of pieces of apparatus have to be included, it is quite usual to represent them in this way.

It would not do to adopt such a method with everything, as the object of the symbols is to show as far as possible the correct connections of terminals, battery poles, and so on.